HOW SWEET THE SOUND

HYMNS FOR PIANO DUET

ARRANGED BY H. E. SINGLEY

FOREWORD

The hymn and gospel song arrangements in this book are based on melodies that will be readily known in most evangelical churches throughout the English-speaking world. In fact, the melodies contained herein are familiar to believers in other language situations as well. As such, I trust these settings will be an asset to the ministry of music wherever they may be used.

The players should always be conscious of where the melody lies in the arrangement and seek to tastefully bring it out as much as possible.

These piano duets are dedicated to God's glory and to my wife, Noretta, with whom I have been privileged to perform these arrangements throughout the Americas.

H. E. Singley

CONTENTS

Our Great Savior

SECONDO

ROWLAND H. PRICHARD
Arr. by H. E. Singley

Our Great Savior

PRIMO

ROWLAND H. PRICHARD
Arr. by H. E. Singley

SECONDO

PRIMO

8va
21
8va
mf
25
29
mp
34
39

SECONDO

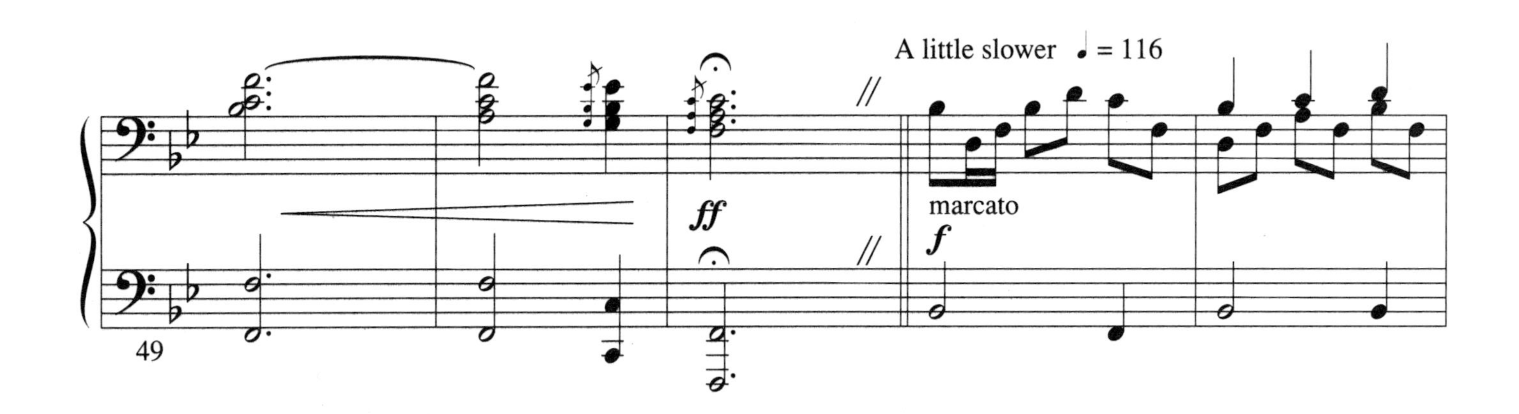

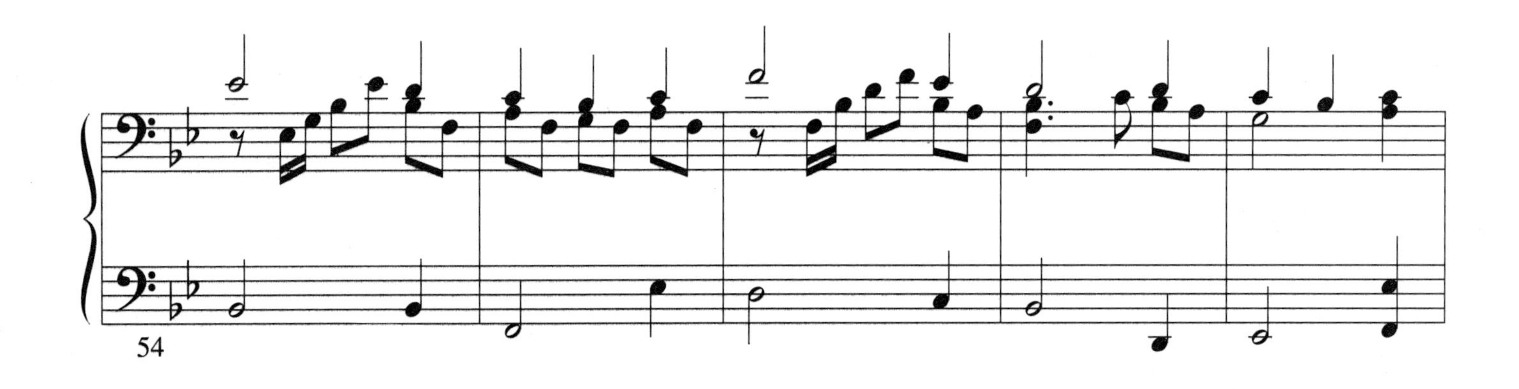

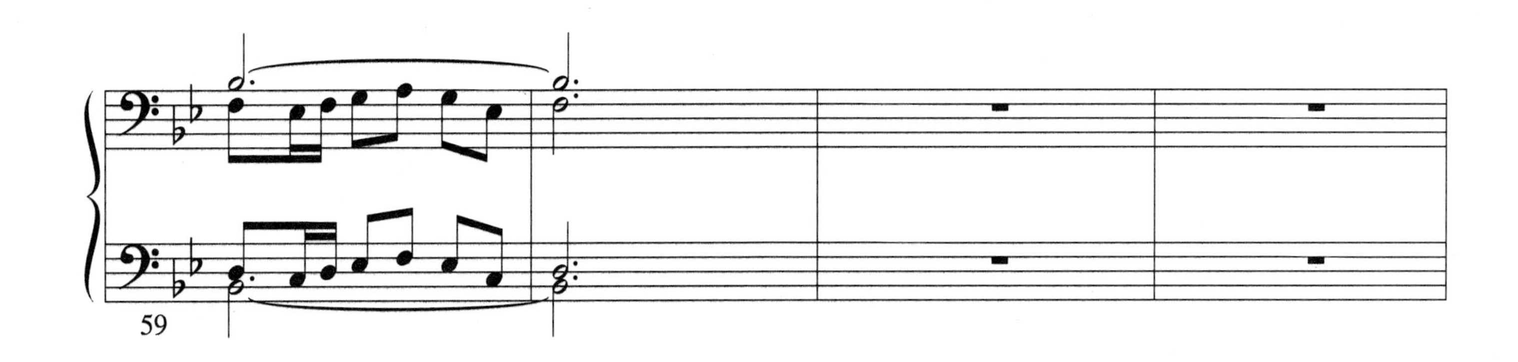

PRIMO

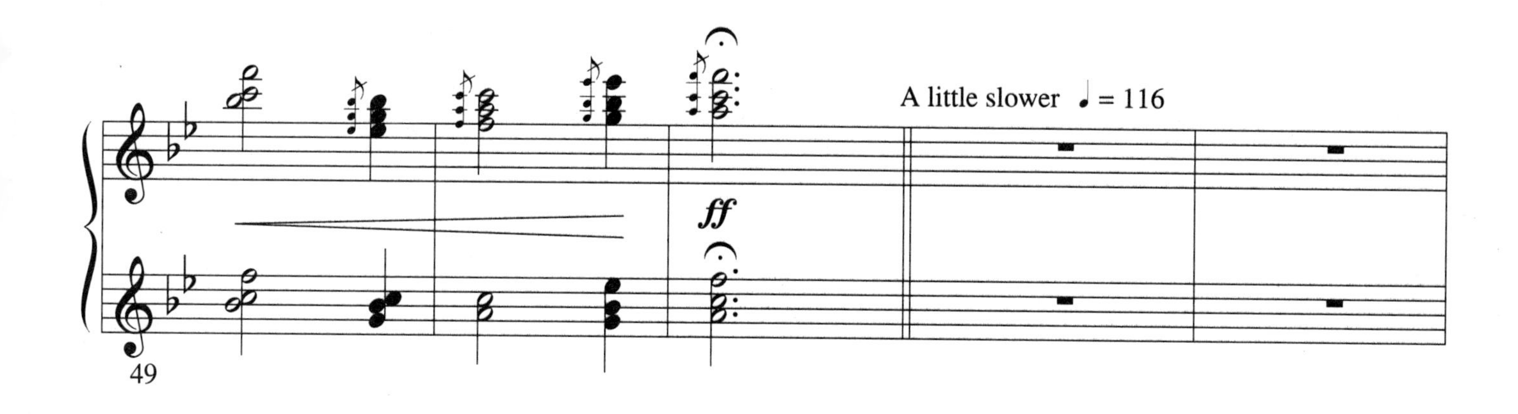

SECONDO

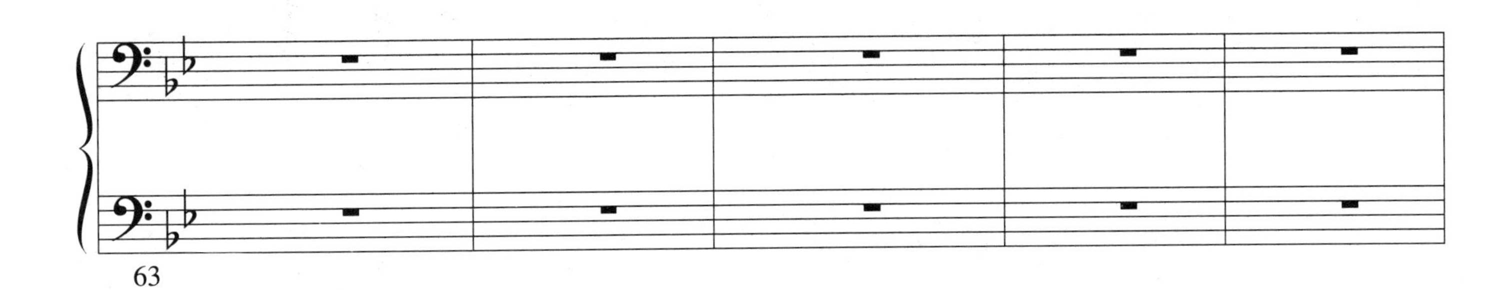

PRIMO

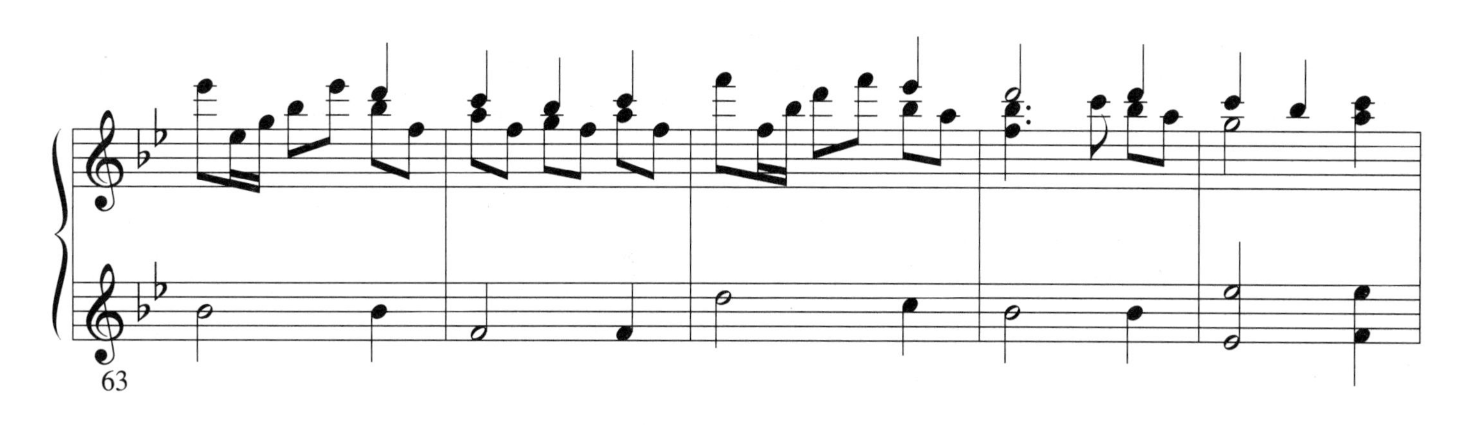

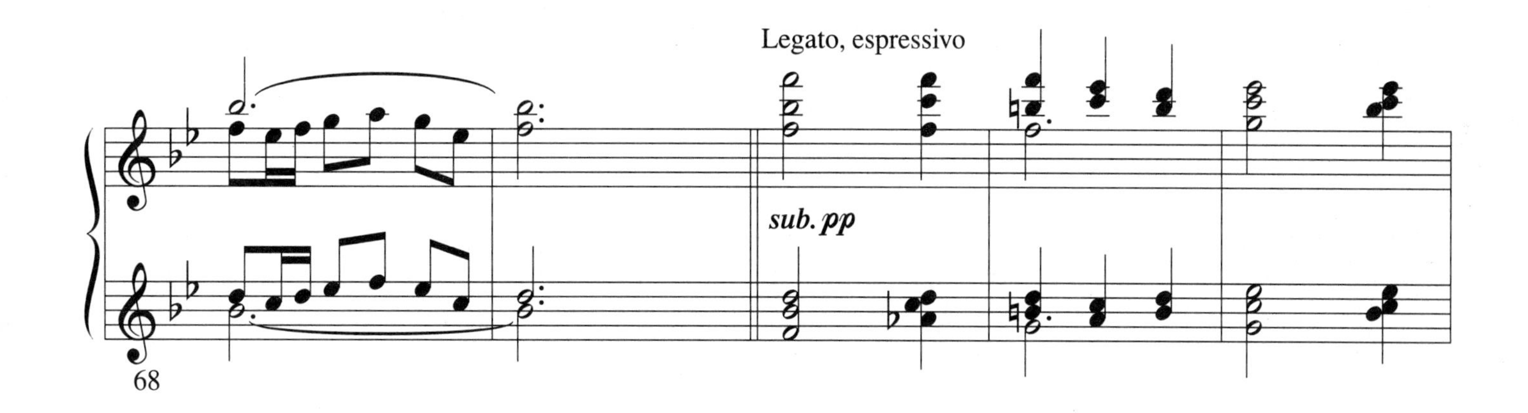

SECONDO

PRIMO

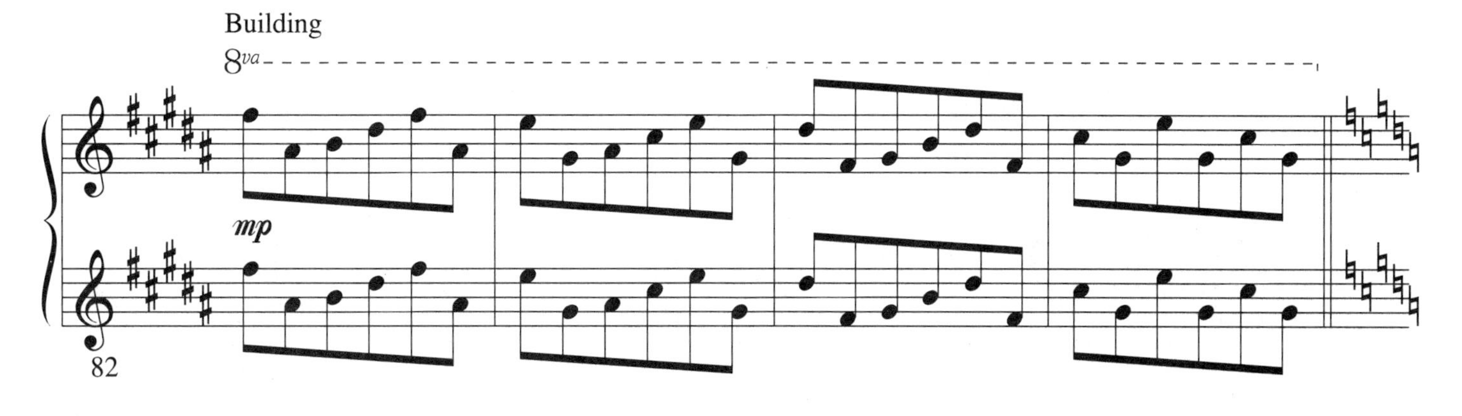

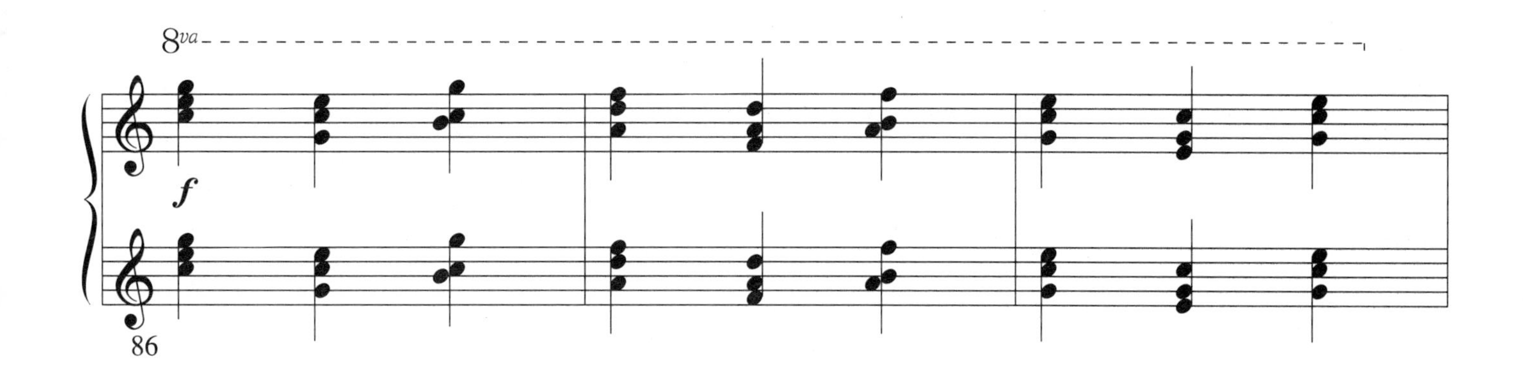

SECONDO

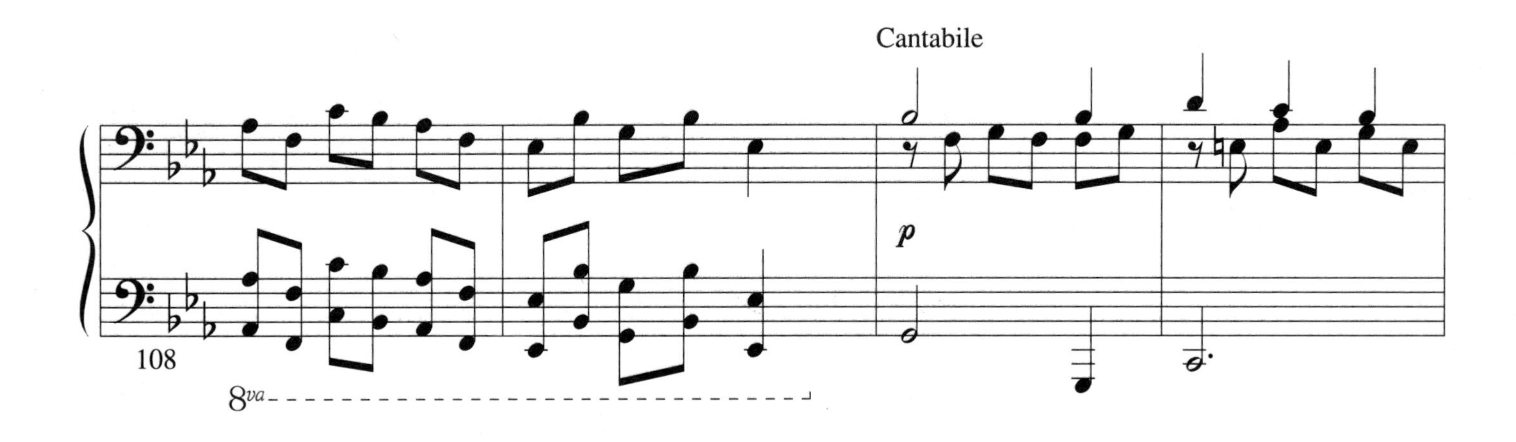

PRIMO

8va
f
99

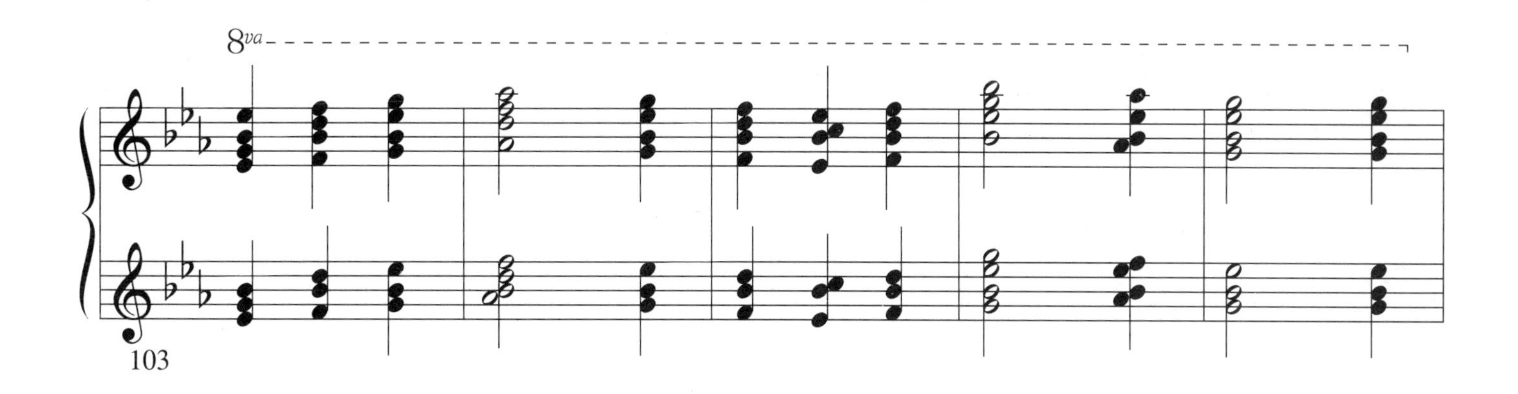
8va
103

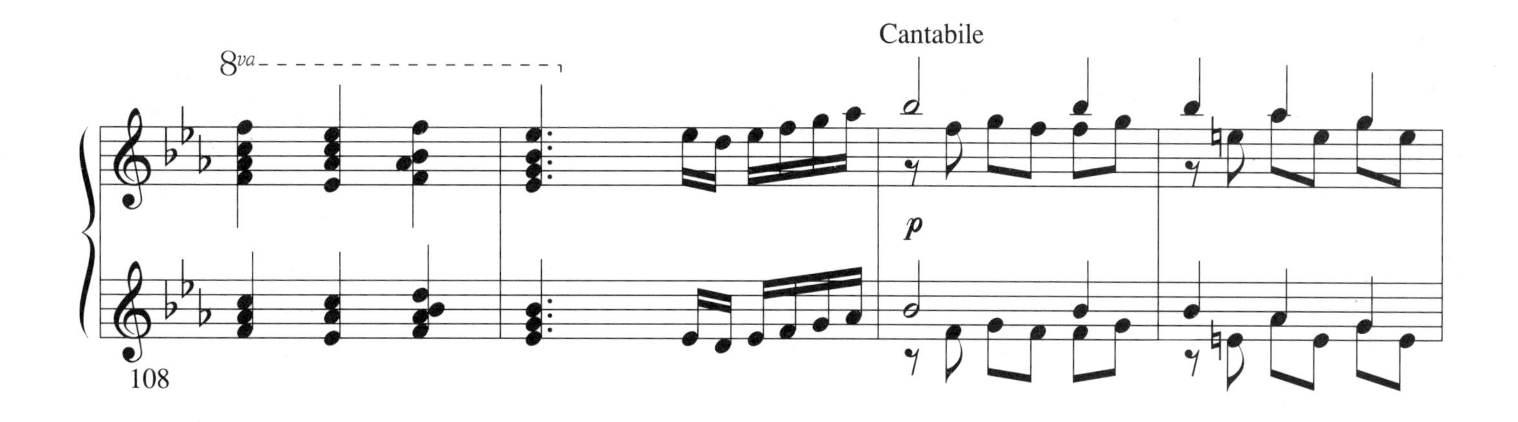
8va
Cantabile
p
108

112

SECONDO

PRIMO

And Can It Be?

SECONDO

THOMAS CAMPBELL
Arr. by H. E. Singley

Majestically ♩ = 112

ff

8va

1

Delicately

poco rit.

mp
a tempo

5

8

8va

11

8va

p

And Can It Be?

PRIMO

THOMAS CAMPBELL
Arr. by H. E. Singley

SECONDO

PRIMO

SECONDO

PRIMO

8va
31

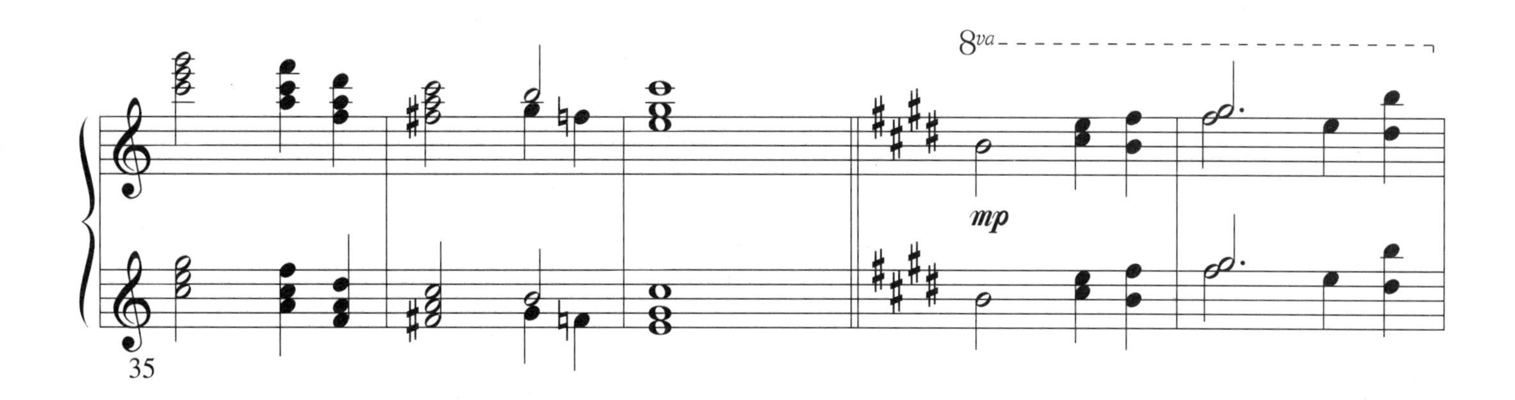
8va
mp
35

8va
40

8va
p
f
p
45

SECONDO

PRIMO

SECONDO

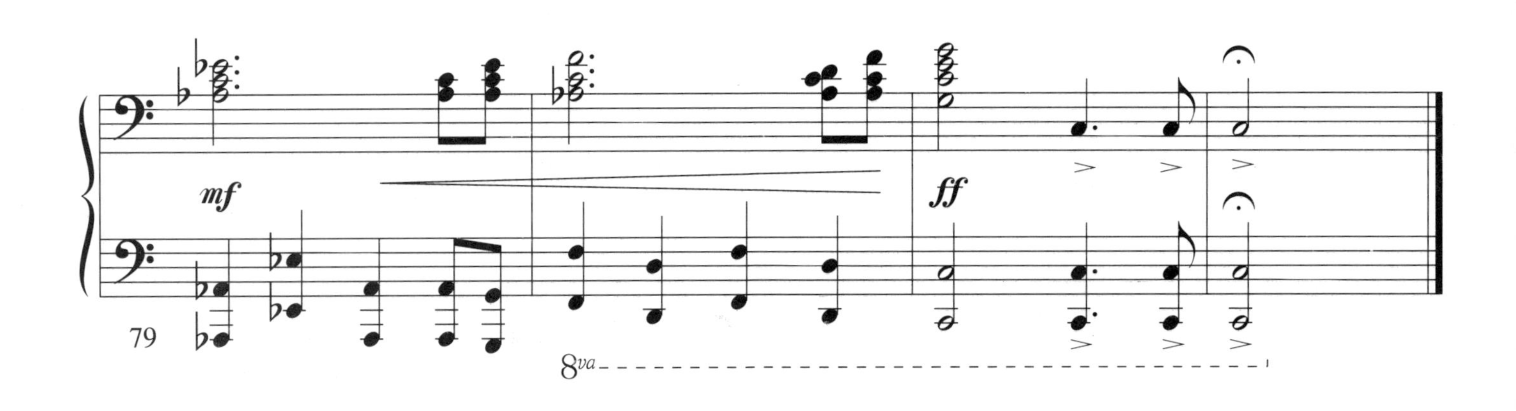

PRIMO

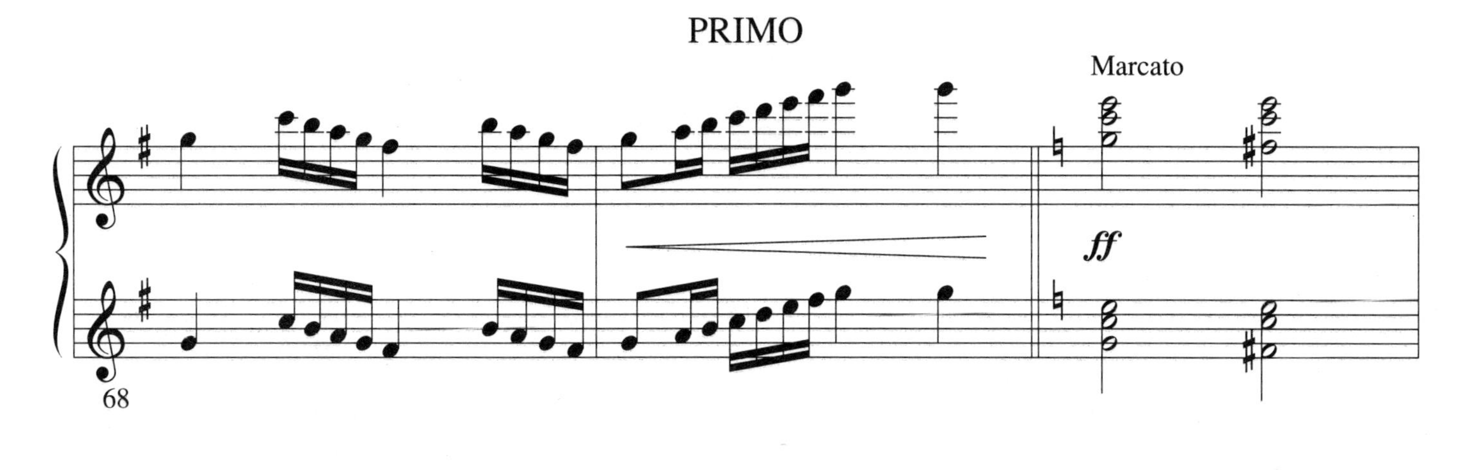

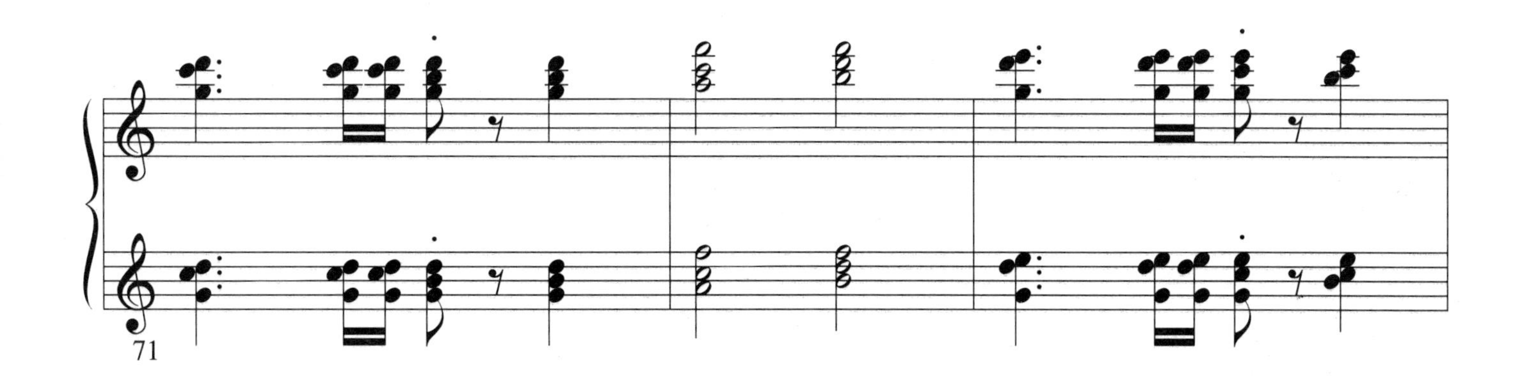

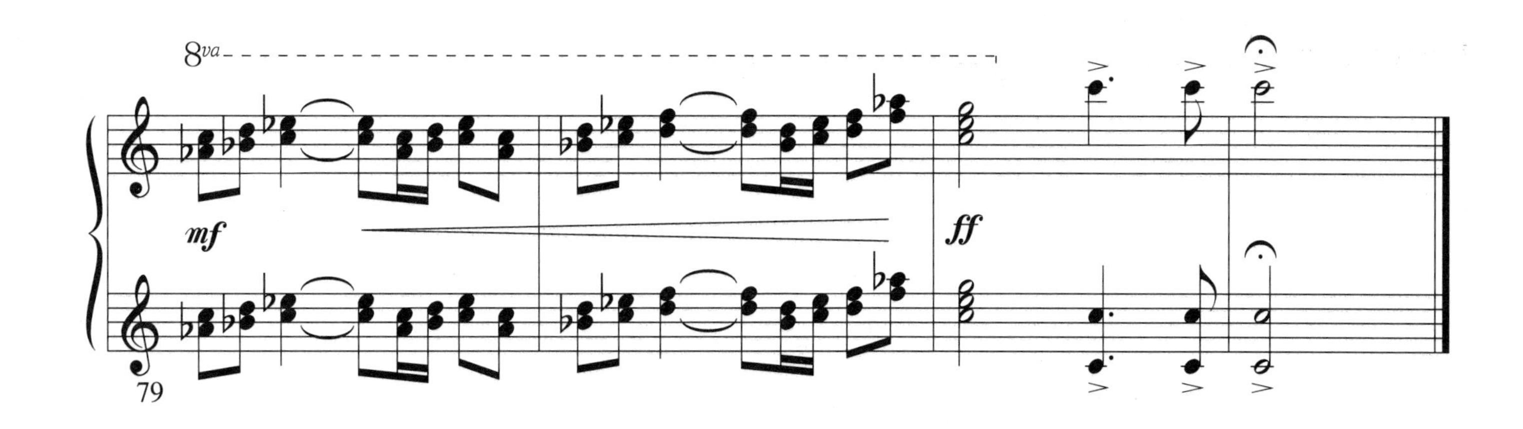

Amazing Grace

SECONDO

From *Virginia Harmony, 1831*
Arr. by H. E. Singley

Amazing Grace

PRIMO

From *Virginia Harmony, 1831*
Arr. by H. E. Singley

Reverently ♩ = 84

SECONDO

PRIMO

SECONDO

PRIMO

SECONDO

PRIMO

SECONDO

PRIMO

Immortal, Invisible, God Only Wise

SECONDO

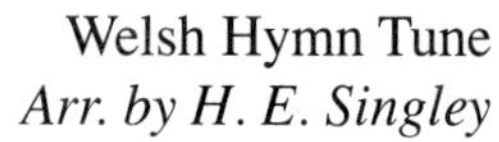

Immortal, Invisible, God Only Wise

PRIMO

Welsh Hymn Tune
Arr. by H. E. Singley

SECONDO

PRIMO

8va
f
17
8va
21
8va
sub. mp
mp
25
8va
mp
29

SECONDO

PRIMO

SECONDO

PRIMO

SECONDO

PRIMO

O Worship the King

SECONDO

JOHANN MICHAEL HAYDN
Arr. by H. E. Singley

O Worship the King

PRIMO

JOHANN MICHAEL HAYDN
Arr. by H. E. Singley

SECONDO

PRIMO

SECONDO

Slower, more freely
p
37
poco rit.
mp
p
mp
a tempo
cresc.
43
mf
p
poco rit.
48
Tempo I
p
53

PRIMO

8va
Slower, more freely
p
37

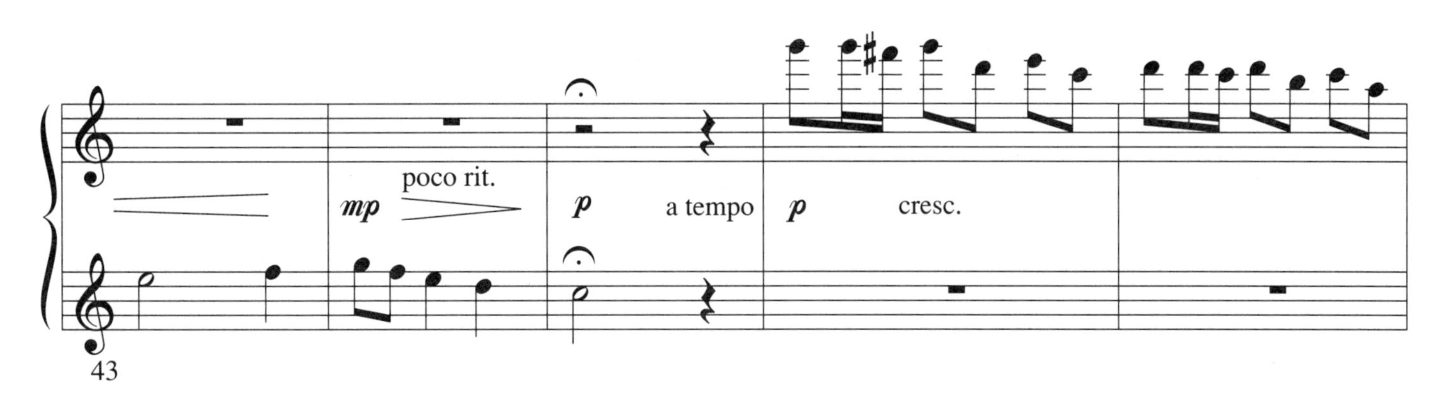
mp
poco rit.
p
a tempo
p
cresc.
43

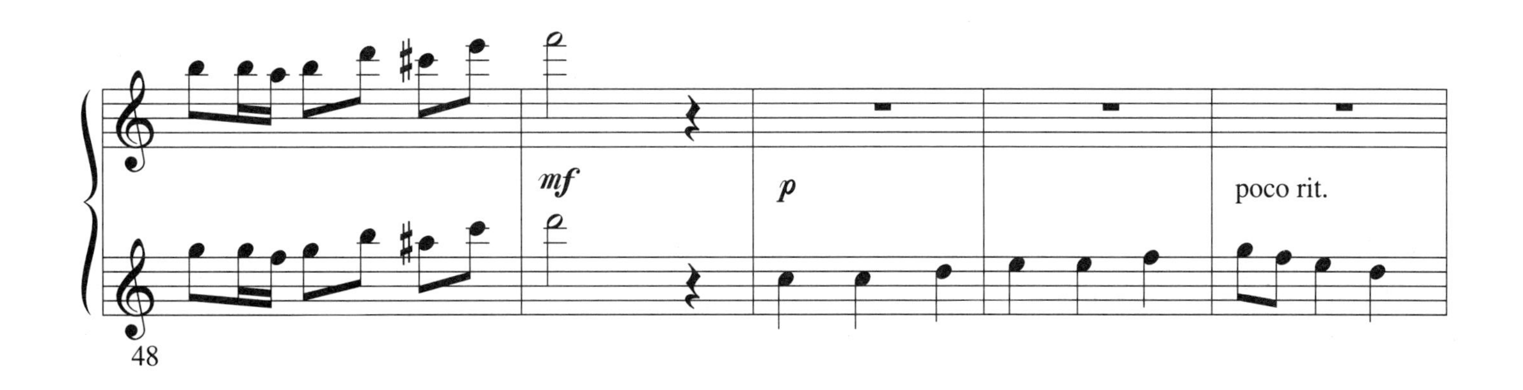
mf
p
poco rit.
48

Tempo I
p
53

SECONDO

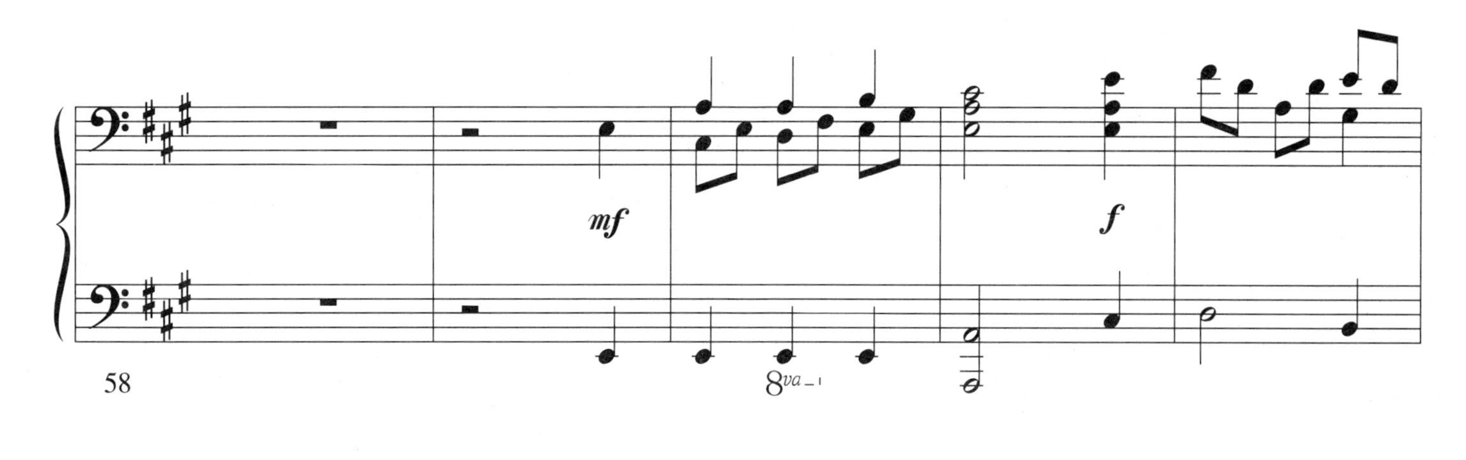

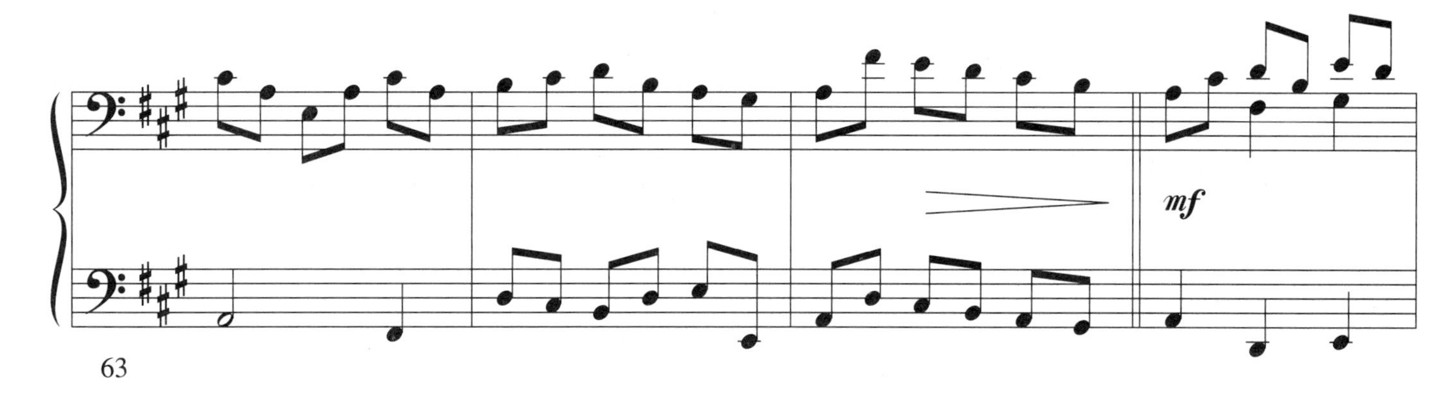

PRIMO

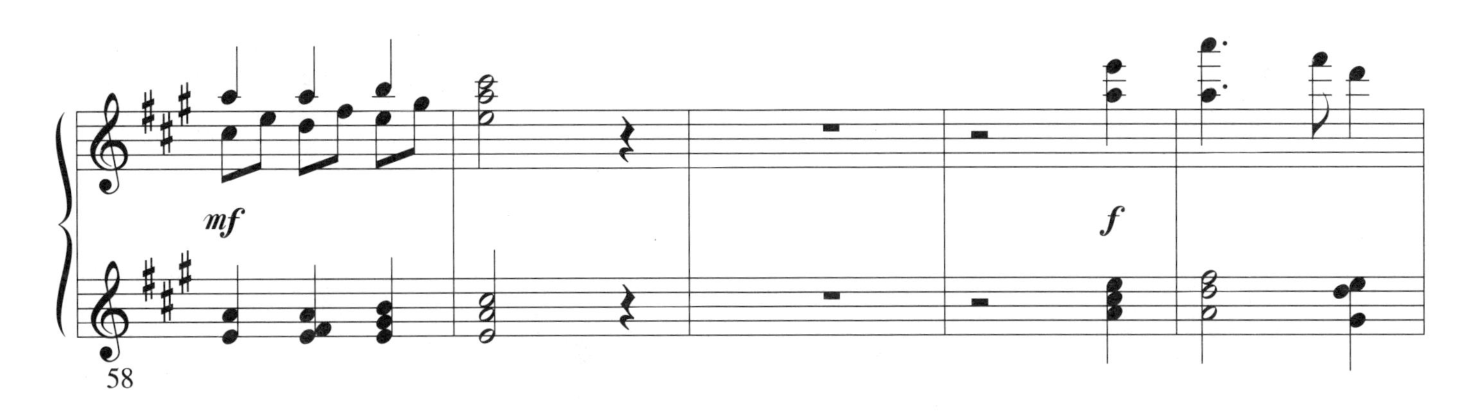

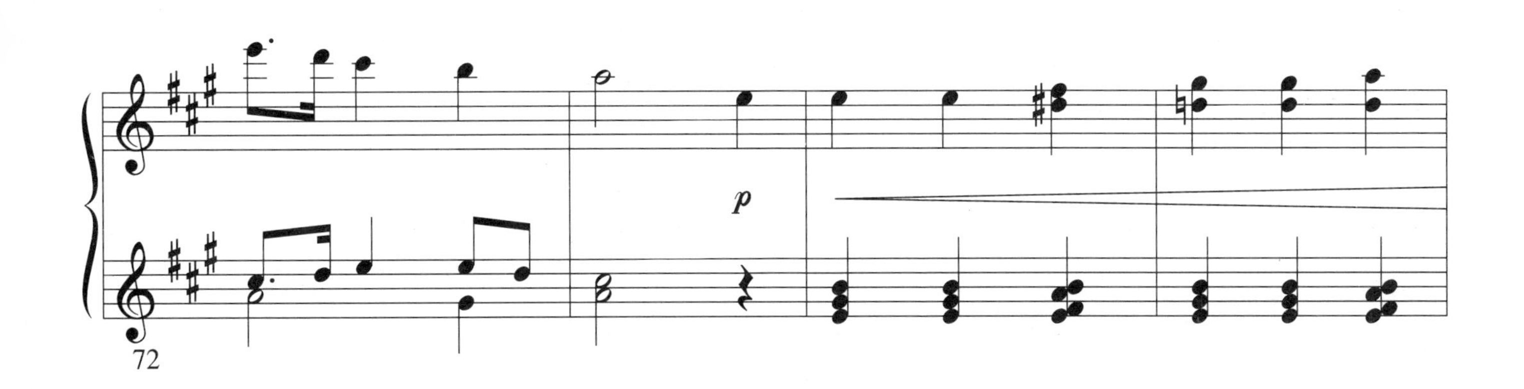

SECONDO

PRIMO

Revive Us Again

SECONDO

JOHN J. HUSBAND
Arr. by H. E. Singley

Revive Us Again

PRIMO

JOHN J. HUSBAND
Arr. by H. E. Singley

Joyfully ♩ = 104

8va

mf *ff* *mf* *f*

1 6 11 16

SECONDO

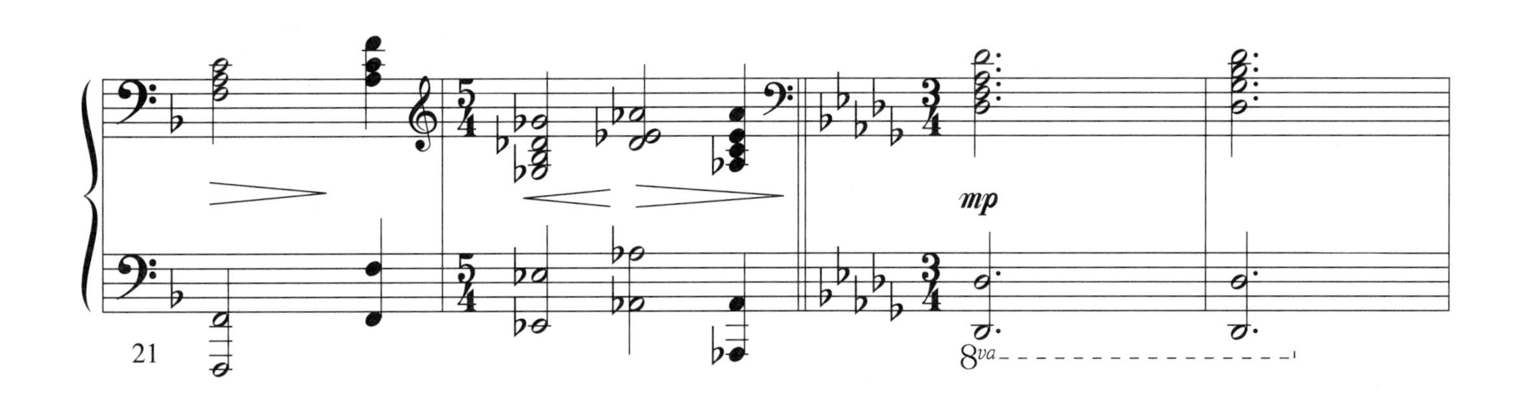

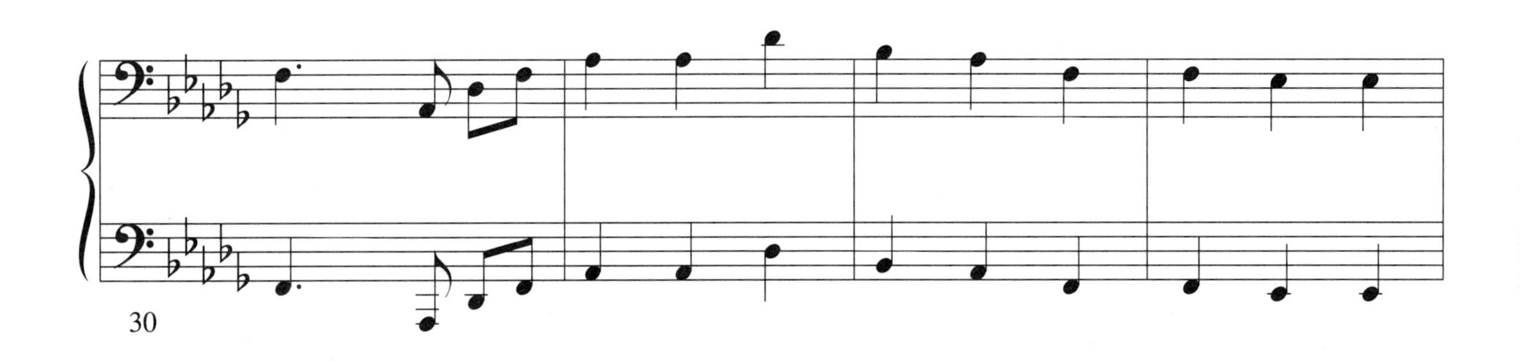

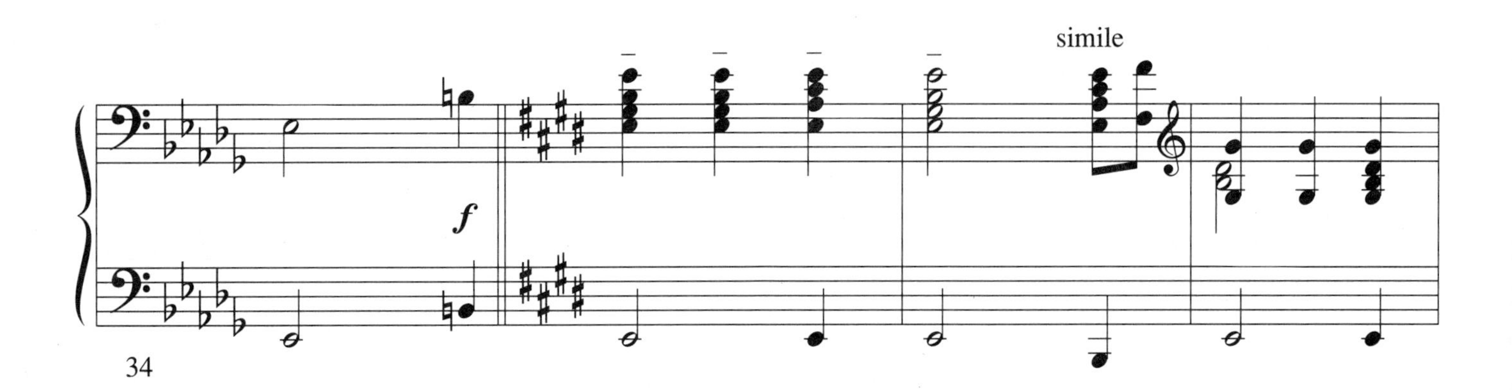

PRIMO

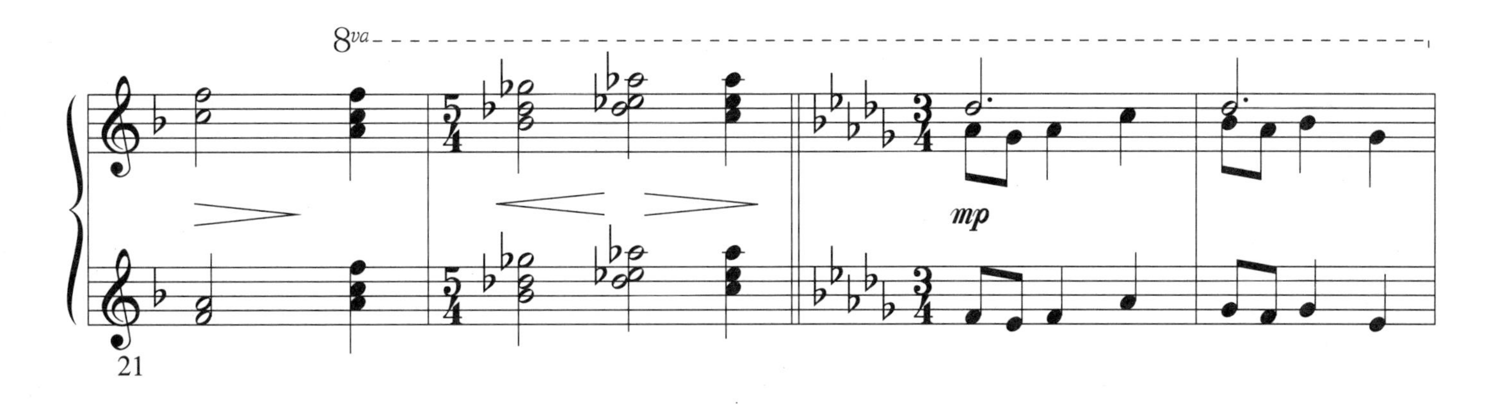

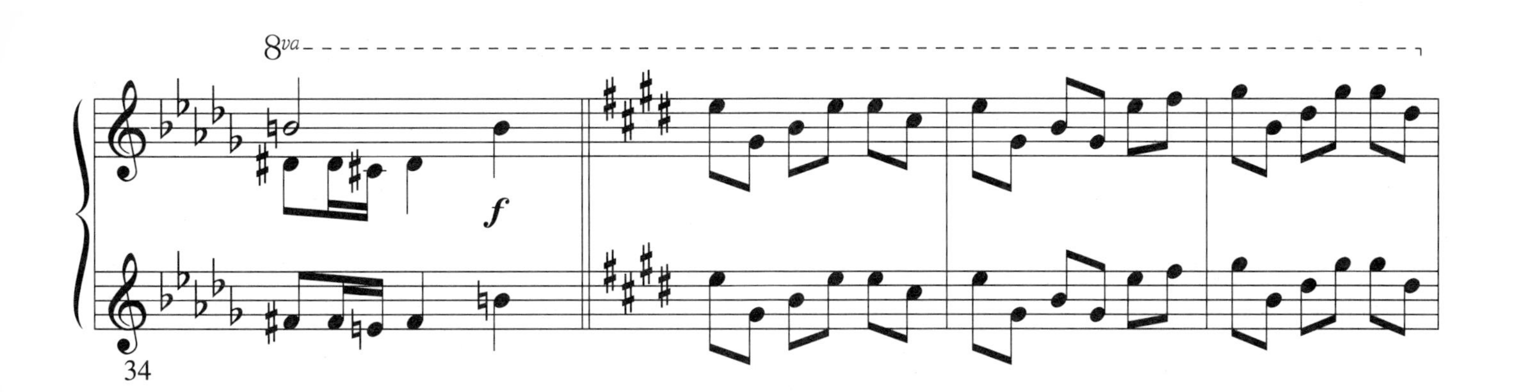

SECONDO

PRIMO

SECONDO

53
58
ff
sub. p
ff
sub. p
62
ff
sub. p
f
8va
66
cresc. poco a poco
rit.
ff
8va
8va
8va
8va

PRIMO

3
3
53

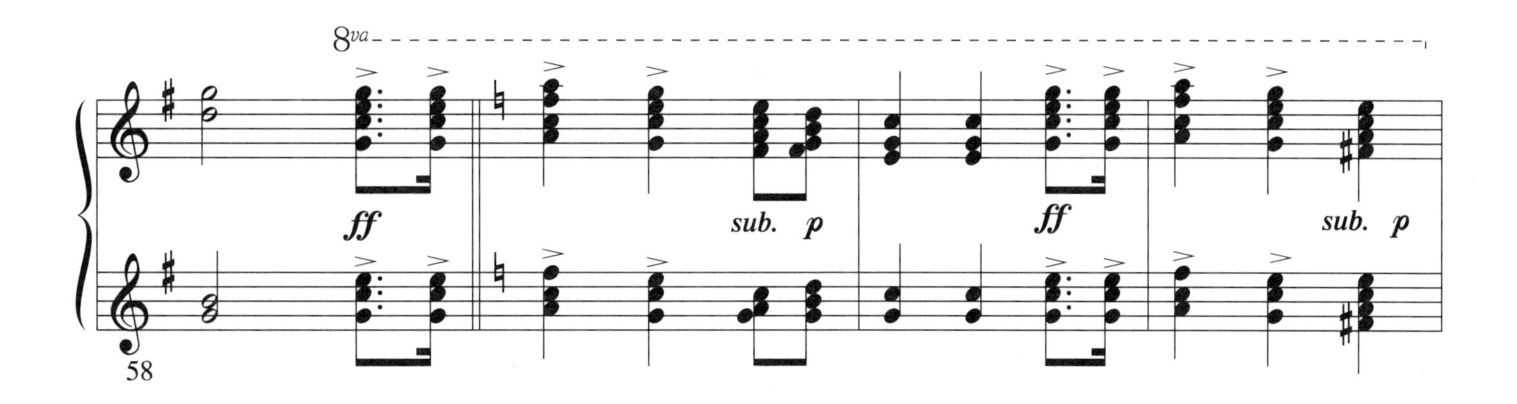
8va
ff
sub. p
ff
sub. p
58

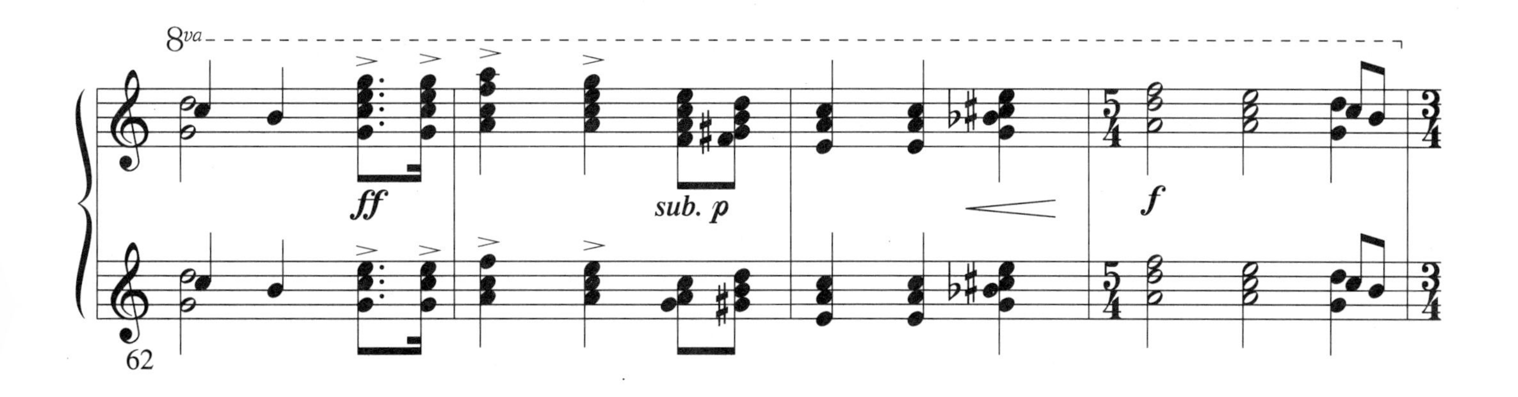
8va
ff
sub. p
f
62

8va
cresc. poco a poco
rit.
ff
66

Alleluia

SECONDO

JERRY SINCLAIR
Arr. by H. E. Singley

With sensitivity ♩ = 60

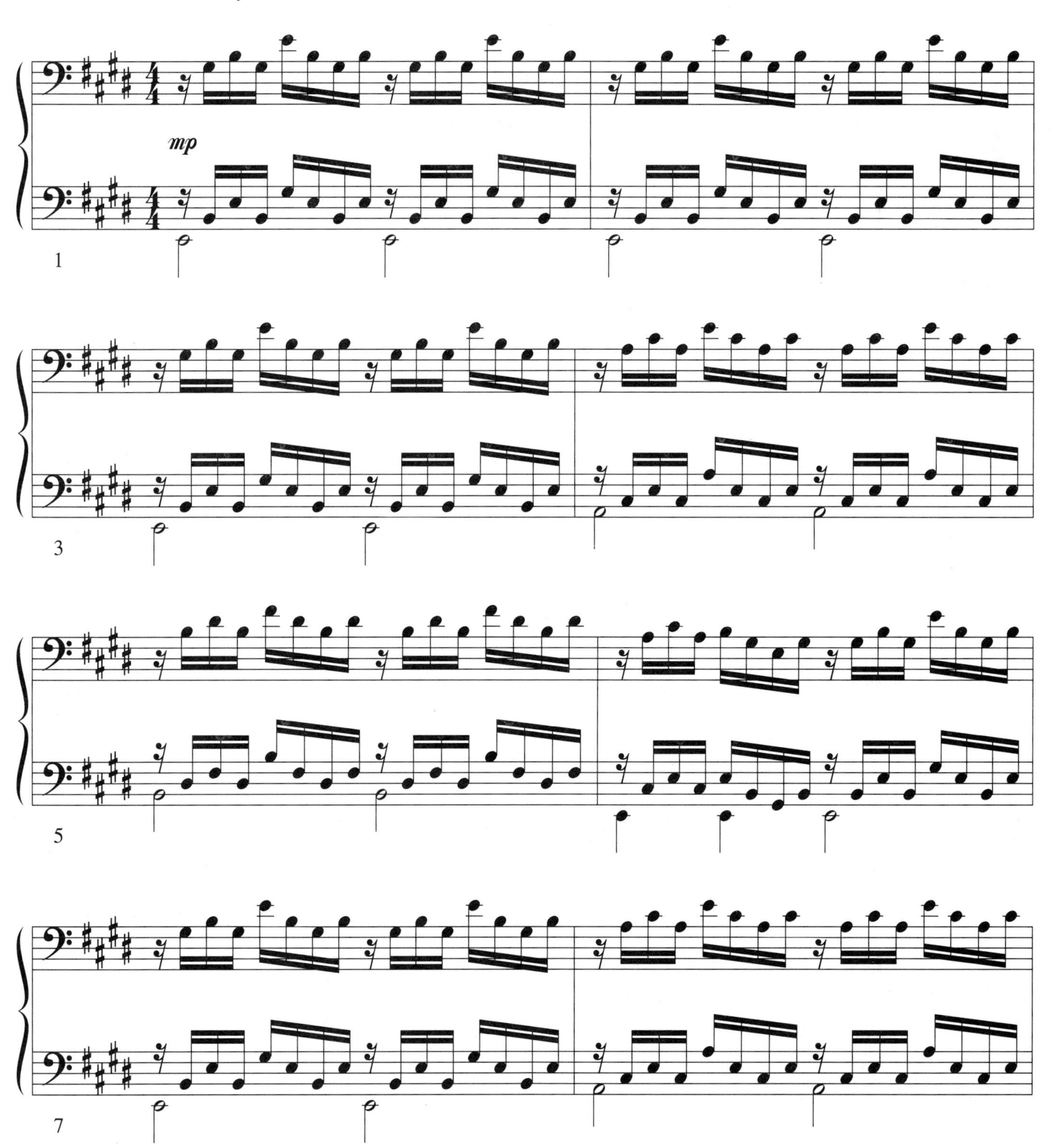

Alleluia

PRIMO

JERRY SINCLAIR
Arr. by H. E. Singley

SECONDO

PRIMO

SECONDO

PRIMO

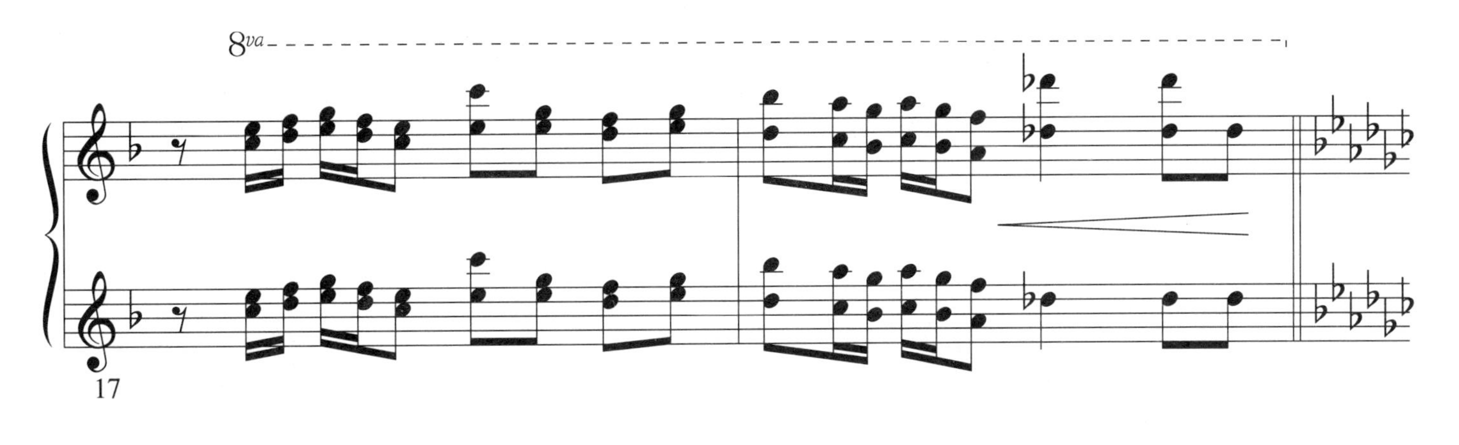
8va
17

Both hands 8va
f
19

Both hands 8va
22

Both hands 8va
molto rit.
24